THE SELFISH SHELLFISH

WIL

LIBRARY & I

To Pookie

THE SELFISH
SHELLFISH

David Wood

AMBER LANE PRESS

First published in 1983 by
Amber Lane Press Ltd
9 Middle Way
Oxford OX2 7LH

Printed in Great Britain
by Cotswold Press Ltd, Oxford

Copyright © David Wood, 1983
Photographs copyright © Format Photography,
Godalming, Surrey

The music for *The Selfish Shellfish*, composed by David Wood, is available
from Samuel French Ltd, 52 Fitzroy Street, London W1P 6JR. Please
note that no other music, specially composed or otherwise, may be used.

ISBN 0 906399 44 0

The Selfish Shellfish was originally commissioned by The Redgrave Theatre, Farnham. The first performance was given by the Farnham Repertory Company on 29 March 1983, with the following cast:

SEAGULL	Paul Benzing
MUSSEL	Peter Geddis
H.C.	John Hughes
URCHIN	Pauline Little
STARFISH	Judith Carlisle
SLUDGE	Viv Parsons
THE GREAT SLICK	Michael G. Jones

Director:	Stephen Barry
Musical Director:	Simon Lowe
Designer:	Kate Robertson
Lighting Designer:	Paul Denby
Stage Management:	Anna Lieven

The Selfish Shellfish was subsequently presented at Sadler's Wells Theatre, London and on tour by Whirligig Theatre in the autumn of 1983.

Photographs, from the Redgrave Theatre production, featuring members of the Farnham Repertory Company, courtesy of Format Photography.

CHARACTERS

SEAGULL:	happy-go-lucky, breezy, helpful.
MUSSEL:	tough on the surface, kind at heart. He can retreat into his hinged shell to avoid danger.
H.C.:	MUSSEL's boss. A hermit crab. Elderly, irritable hermit. The selfish shellfish.
URCHIN:	naughty, yet vulnerable 'child' — a sea urchin.
STARFISH:	URCHIN's Auntie. Brash, business-like and physically very strong.
SLUDGE:	an oily advance guard for the GREAT SLICK.
THE GREAT SLICK:	an oil slick. His black cloak is big enough to cover the stage.
THE GIANT ANEMONE:	not played by an actor, but a large puppet-like creature with waving tentacles and ever-hungry mouth.

The play is set in a rockpool — from the point of view of the rockpool creatures. Consequently the set is on a larger-than-life scale.

PROLOGUE

The actors, in rehearsal dress, assemble on stage while the audience is arriving. Some could welcome individual members of the audience. Others could be putting on make-up, or putting the final touches to the set. The impression should be that the actors are getting ready to perform.

With the house lights still up, a musician starts playing. One by one the actors stop what they are doing and assemble in a group.

Song: **When will we learn?**

When will we learn?
When will we learn?
That the world
Wasn't made
For only you and me?
When will we learn?
When will it be?
When will we learn?
When will we see?

> [*The music continues. Some actors hum the tune. Others speak over it. The following speeches could be taken by one actor, or divided amongst several.*]

ACTOR/S: On the earth there are hundreds of thousands of different kinds of creatures.

Animals.
Fish.
Birds.
Insects.
But human beings are the cleverest.
At any rate, we *think* we are.
That's why we run the world. We may argue amongst ourselves *how* we should run it, but we have that power, because we are so clever.
But sometimes we make mistakes.
We're only human . . .
And the cleverer we become, the bigger the mistakes we can make.
The cleverer we are, the more inventive we are, the more we try to improve the world, the more problems we create.
Not only for ourselves. But also for all the creatures who share the earth with us.
We'd like to tell you a story, not a true story exactly, but perhaps it could be.
About some creatures whose lives are changed by the cleverness, the foolishness of human beings.
Imagine we're at the seaside.
> [*Lighting and sound effects. The actors finish preparing the set.*]

Imagine a rock pool.
> [*More lighting.*]

Imagine the sea.
> [*Actors cover the set with a silken sheet, to represent the sea.*]

And we'll tell you the story of . . .
THE SELFISH SHELLFISH.

Song: **When will we learn?**

> [*As they sing, actors prepare for the play. The actor playing* SEAGULL *is dressed in his costume, which is representative rather than realistic.*]

ALL: When will we learn?
When will we learn?
That the world
Wasn't made
For only you and me?
When will we learn?
When will it be?
When will we learn?
When will we see?

> [*The actors 'disappear'. The music continues.*]

> [*House lights fade.*]

ACT ONE

*Dramatic sound and lighting effects as the tide goes out.
The silken sheet suggests the waves retreating. Perhaps
the actors manipulate it.*

 *Lighting increases to suggest a sunny afternoon. The
rockpool is revealed: a roughly circular pool with fairly
high rocks at the back, sloping down towards the front.
Downstage the rocks are low, with a suggestion of shingly
beach at the very edge.*

 *Some of the high rocks are coated with seaweed,
including clumps of hanging bladderwrack, behind
which are crevices affording hiding places. Attached to
and almost part of the rocks to one side (but not too far
upstage) is a large dog whelk shell, in which* H.C., *the
hermit crab, lives.·The opening has a door with 'H.C.'
written on. To the other side is the* GIANT ANEMONE,
*complete with tentacles and an expandable opening
(mouth) through which food can be thrown or a large
object 'sucked'. This could be operated by a stagehand.*

 *The floor of the pool should suggest water and sand
or shingle, plus the odd rock. One area of rocks to one side
upstage should be graduated enough for a large object to
be rolled over and out of vision.*

 *An assortment of human debris litters the rock
pool.The two largest objects are an old tin can, its lid still
'hinged', and the sole of an old rubber 'flip-flop'-type
shoe. The can must be big enough to accommodate two
characters; the flip-flop sole will be used as a stretcher on
which to carry a character. Other items of debris washed*

up could include a cork, bits of driftwood, cuttlefish, a crisp packet, a bottle-top, etc., plus seaweed.

MUSSEL *is lying inert, virtually undetectable, fairly near the whelk shell. Music as* SEAGULL *enters over the back of the rocks. He flaps his wings and takes deep breaths. He moves down into the pool and occasionally pecks for food.*

SEAGULL: *[calls]* What ho! Anyone about? *[He looks about. No reaction.]* Any chance of a fishy tea?
    [No reaction. He pecks around for food.]
    [seeing something] Ah. Bingo!
    [He pecks at some rubbish — maybe the crisp packet.]
    [realising it is inedible] Ugh! Yuck!
    [He goes elsewhere.]
    [seeing something] Ah. Bingo!
    [He pecks at something — perhaps the cork. His beak could get embedded in it.]
    [struggling] Ahhhhh! *[getting rid of it]* Yuck, yuck, yuck.
    [He goes to MUSSEL.*]*
  Ah. Bingo!
    [He pecks MUSSEL. *Another peck.* MUSSEL *moves.* SEAGULL *goes to peck again.* MUSSEL *jumps up.* SEAGULL *is surprised.]*

MUSSEL: Oi! What's your game?

SEAGULL: I beg your pardon?

MUSSEL: Not granted. What do you want?

SEAGULL: Well, I was rather hoping for a fishy tea.

MUSSEL: A fishy tea? Me?

SEAGULL: Well, yes. You look rather tasty.
    [He goes to peck again.]

MUSSEL: Get off! You keep your greedy beak to yourself.

SEAGULL: There's no need to be rude.

MUSSEL: You can't eat me!

SEAGULL: Why not?

MUSSEL: I'm a mussel.

SEAGULL: I like mussels.

MUSSEL: Well, you wouldn't like me.

SEAGULL: I don't think anyone would like you. You're extremely rude.

MUSSEL: You wouldn't like me 'cos I'm tough, see? Tough. So don't try anything. Clear off.

SEAGULL: All right, all right. Stop flapping.

MUSSEL: I'm not flapping.

SEAGULL: You are.

MUSSEL: You're the one who'd better start flapping, mate. Flap your wings and fly away. Sharpish.
[H.C. *suddenly opens his door and emerges from his shell, waving his claws.*]

H.C.: What's all this racket?

SEAGULL: [*to* MUSSEL] Temper, temper.

MUSSEL: [*shouting*] Clear off.

H.C.: Quiet!

SEAGULL: [*to* MUSSEL] Calm down!

MUSSEL: I'm perfectly calm. Clear off!

H.C.: *Quiet!*
[SEAGULL *and* MUSSEL *hear him.*]

MUSSEL: [*almost springing to attention*] Sorry, H.C.

H.C.: I've never heard such a dreadful din.

MUSSEL: Sorry, H.C.

H.C.: I'm trying to think.

MUSSEL: Sorry, H.C.

H.C.: Stop saying, 'Sorry, H.C.'

MUSSEL: Sorry, H.C. [*realising*] Whoops.

SEAGULL: Who's your friend?

MUSSEL: He's not my friend. He's my boss. H.C.
SEAGULL: I'd gathered that. [*to* H.C.] Good afternoon . . . er, H.C.?
MUSSEL: H.C. Stands for Hermit Crab.
H.C.:   And one thing H.C. *doesn't* stand for is strangers in this rockpool.
          [*He poses threateningly.*]
SEAGULL: Ah.
H.C.:   What do you want?
SEAGULL: Well, I was explaining to your, er, colleague. I was hoping for a fishy tea.
MUSSEL: He tried to eat *me*.
H.C.:   Why?
SEAGULL: Well, it's teatime.
H.C.:   Is it?
SEAGULL: Certainly. The tide's gone out.
H.C.:   Where's my tea, Mussel?
MUSSEL: Eh?
H.C.:   My tea. Where is it?
MUSSEL: Just getting it, H.C. At the double, H.C.
          [*He rushes off and finds a cockle-shaped bowl of food under the rocks, behind the seaweed.*]
SEAGULL: Ah. Useful chap, Mussel.
H.C.:   He does as he's told. [*meaningfully*] Not too chatty.
SEAGULL: Quite. Er . . . no chanee of joining you for tea?
H.C.:   No chance. I don't like company.
SEAGULL: O.K. Fair enough. [*He starts to go.*] Be seeing you.
H.C.:   I hope not.
          [SEAGULL *sets off upstage.* MUSSEL *returns with the food, and puts it down.*]
MUSSEL: Tea, H.C.
          [H.C. *is looking at the rockpool.*]
H.C.:   What on earth is that?
MUSSEL: Your usual, H.C. Plankton and seaweed stew.

H.C.: Not that, you moronic mussel. *That!*
[*He makes his way towards the tin can.*]

MUSSEL: Big Ones' rubbish, H.C. Tin can. Tide brought it.
[*He follows behind.*]

H.C.: Mmm.

[*As both investigate the outside of the tin can,*
SEAGULL, *who has been quietly hanging around,*
creeps back. Music accompanies his tiptoeing to
the food bowl. He gulps down the food, then
returns to the rocks, looking innocent. H.C. *and*
MUSSEL *return.*]

Litterbugs. Filthy litterbugs. [*He looks up and shouts:*]
Leave your wretched rubbish somewhere else, Big
Ones!

[*He picks up his food bowl. He goes to eat, but*
finds no food.]

[*sharp*] Mussel. Where's my tea?

MUSSEL: I gave it to you, H.C.

H.C.: Well, it's not here.

MUSSEL: Sorry, H.C.

[*Bemused, he goes to get some more. He sees*
SEAGULL. SEAGULL *waves politely.*]

SEAGULL: Just on my way.

[MUSSEL *goes to speak, but is interrupted.*]

H.C.: Hurry, Mussel, I'm hungry.

MUSSEL: Coming, H.C.

[*He collects more food and returns. He puts it*
down. H.C. *has seen the flip-flop sole.*]

H.C.: What on earth is *that?*

MUSSEL: I told you, H.C. Plankton and sea —

H.C.: Not that. *That!*

[*He advances on the sole, followed by* MUSSEL.
Music as SEAGULL *again seizes his opportunity.*
He creeps up to the food and eats it, then nips

> *away and stands innocently.* MUSSEL *and* H.C.
> *have picked up the sole.*]

H.C.: What is it?

MUSSEL: Bit of a Big One's shoe, I think, H.C. We've seen them before.

> [*They start to return.*]

H.C.: Well we don't want to see it again, do we? Get rid of it, Mussel.

MUSSEL: Right, H.C.

H.C.: [*indicating the can*] And that.

MUSSEL: Right, H.C.

> [H.C. *goes for his food. He finds it gone.*]

H.C.: Mussel.

MUSSEL: Yes, H.C.?

H.C.: I'm starting to simmer. Where's my tea?

MUSSEL: I gave it to you, H.C. Twice.

H.C.: And twice I haven't had it.

MUSSEL: Sorry, H.C. I'll get some more.

> [*He goes to get more, and again sees* SEAGULL. *This time* SEAGULL *keeps his back turned.* MUSSEL *is suspicious. He returns, puts down the food.*]

[*deliberately*] Your tea, H.C.

> [H.C. *goes to take it.*]

[*whispers*] Psssst.

H.C.: Eh?

MUSSEL: Psssst.

H.C.: Don't you psssst me.

MUSSEL: Come over here, H.C. Please.

H.C.: No. I want my . . .

MUSSEL: *Please.*

H.C.: Oh, very well.

> [*They walk away, but* MUSSEL *indicates behind, as if to say 'Watch out for Seagull'.*]

Are you feeling all right?

MUSSEL: Shhh.

[*Music as* SEAGULL *again creeps forward to steal the food. In the nick of time,* MUSSEL *turns, sees, and attacks.*]

Clear off, you thieving great bird.

[SEAGULL *laughs and goes up the rocks and away.*]

SEAGULL: Ha, ha. Toodle oo! Ha, ha. Good afternoon!

MUSSEL: Good riddance. [*pointing to the food*] Tea, H.C.

H.C.: Thank you, Mussel. Well done.

[MUSSEL *yawns and starts to close up his shell and lie down.*]

What are you doing?

MUSSEL: Thought I'd have a quick kip, H.C.

H.C.: Certainly not. You've got work to do. Clear all this Big Ones' rubbish up.

MUSSEL: Right, H.C.

[H.C. *retires into his shell, and shuts his door.*]

[*Music as* MUSSEL *starts clearing rubbish. He throws a couple of pieces of driftwood over the rocks. Suddenly, a roaring noise. The* GIANT ANEMONE *starts swaying and waving its tentacles. Its mouth opens and shuts.*]

Oh, you've woken up, have you? You want *your* tea?

[*The* GIANT ANEMONE *roars an affirmative reply.*]

Hang on.

[*He finds some food behind the seaweed and takes aim. Music echoes this. He throws the food into the* GIANT ANEMONE's *mouth. Loud munching noises. A rude burping noise.*]

More?

[*The* GIANT ANEMONE *roars.* MUSSEL *gets some more food, takes aim and throws. Loud munching noises.* MUSSEL *slightly loses his balance and falls towards the* GIANT ANEMONE, *whose tentacles stretch out to reach him.*]

Here, watch it!

[*He backs away.*]

Don't you bite the mussel that feeds you.

[*The* GIANT ANEMONE *roars.*]

If you sting me and put me out of action, you'll never get fed. Right?

[*The* GIANT ANEMONE *grudgingly voices its agreement.*]

So watch it. Now, where were we . . . ?

[*Music as he starts clearing up more rubbish. Perhaps he uses an old stick to spike up paper.*]

[*He is stopped in his tracks by a new noise. The sound of crying, sobbing. After a few seconds the noise stops.* MUSSEL *shrugs and carries on with his work. The sobbing noise returns.* MUSSEL *stops and listens. The noise stops.* MUSSEL *shakes his head and starts work again. The noise starts again.* MUSSEL *stops. He looks concerned. He 'sees' the audience, and comes downstage.*]

[*whispering to the audience*] Can you hear something?

AUDIENCE: Yes.

MUSSEL: What is it?

AUDIENCE: Crying.

MUSSEL: Crying?

AUDIENCE: Yes.

MUSSEL: That's what I thought. Funny. Where's it coming from, I wonder?

[*He starts looking around. The sobbing noise*

returns, louder. It is coming from inside the tin can.]

[*Hopefully the audience leads* MUSSEL *to the tin can. He goes in the wrong direction a couple of times, but eventually understands. He listens. The sobbing noise.*]

[*Music echoes the tension as* MUSSEL *gingerly lifts up the hinged, jagged lid. (N.B. the can is on its side.) He peers inside. Sudden crying makes him jump and hesitate, but he looks in again.*]

[*gently*] Hallo? Who's there? Come out.

[*More sobs.*]

I'm not going to hurt you. Come on.

[*Pause. Then, slowly,* URCHIN *emerges. He should look appealingly vulnerable. He looks warily around and at* MUSSEL.]

That's it.

[MUSSEL *goes to comfort him.* URCHIN *screams.*]

It's all right.

[URCHIN *calms a little.*]

You're a sea urchin, aren't you?

[URCHIN *screams, then nods.*]

Hallo, Urchin. I'm Mussel. What were you doing in there? Eh?

[URCHIN *screams.*]

Shh. Shh. Listen, where do you live?

[URCHIN *sobs and shakes his head.*]

You don't know? Are you lost?

URCHIN: [*with a sob*] Aunt.

MUSSEL: Aren't? You *aren't* lost?

[URCHIN *nods.*]

You *are* lost?

URCHIN: *Aunt. Aunt.*

MUSSEL: You *aren't* lost?

> [URCHIN *shakes his head, sobs, then nods.*]
> Well, *I'm* lost. I can't understand you. Come on, try and tell me.

URCHIN: [*with an effort, through the sobs*] Au . . . au . . . aun . . . auntie. Auntie.

MUSSEL: Auntie?

> [URCHIN *nods.*]

URCHIN: I've . . . lost . . . my . . . auntie . . .

> [*More tears.*]

MUSSEL: I see. You've lost your auntie.

> [URCHIN *nods.*]
> Where did you last see her?

URCHIN: In the sea.

MUSSEL: In the sea? When the tide was in?

> [URCHIN *nods.*]
> We'd better have a look for her, eh? She can't be far away. We'll go urchin searchin'! Get it? Urchin searchin'!
>
> [*He tries to make* URCHIN *laugh.* URCHIN *shakes his head.*]
> No?

URCHIN: Auntie's not an urchin.

MUSSEL: Oh. What is she, then? What's she look like?

URCHIN: She's pink with five arms.

MUSSEL: Pink with five arms. Sounds like a riddle. What's pink and got five arms? [*to the audience*] Anyone know?

> [*Hopefully the audience knows. If not,* URCHIN *gives the answer.*]

AUDIENCE: A starfish.

MUSSEL: A what?

AUDIENCE: A starfish.

MUSSEL: A starfish. [*to* URCHIN] Is that right? Is your auntie a starfish?

       [URCHIN *nods.*]

       [*to the audience*] Thanks. [*to* URCHIN] Come on, let's look for her.

       [*Music as* MUSSEL *leads* URCHIN *first of all along the downstage edge of the rockpool.*]

       [*calling*] Auntie Starfish! Auntie Starfish! [*to* URCHIN] Go on, you call her.

       [URCHIN *is reluctant.*]

       Auntie Starfish!

URCHIN: [*tentatively*] Auntie! Auntie Starfish!

MUSSEL: That's it.

URCHIN: [*louder*] Auntie! Auntie Starfish!

       [*They continue looking.*]

BOTH: Auntie Starfish!

       [*They get dangerously near* H.C.*'s shell.*]

       Auntie Starfish!

       [URCHIN *breaks away when he sees the shell and, before* MUSSEL *has a chance to stop him, rushes to the entrance of the shell and shouts very loudly into it.*]

URCHIN: Auntie Starfish!

MUSSEL: No!

       [MUSSEL *sees too late. Suddenly the shell door opens and out pops* H.C., *giving* URCHIN *the shock of his life.*]

H.C.: *Quiet!*

       [URCHIN *rushes to* MUSSEL *for protection.*]

       What's going on?

MUSSEL: Sorry, H.C.

H.C.: What's all this racket? I'm trying to *think.*

MUSSEL: Sorry, H.C.

H.C.: [*distastefully*] Who's *that?*

MUSSEL: Sorry, H.C.

H.C.: And stop saying, 'Sorry, H.C.'

MUSSEL: Sorry, H.C. Whoops. This is Urchin.

H.C.: Urchin? Ugh. How revolting.

MUSSEL: We're searching for his auntie.

H.C.: Well, search elsewhere. She's not here.

MUSSEL: No, H.C. Sorry, H.C. Say sorry to H.C., Urchin.

URCHIN: Shan't.

H.C.: What?

URCHIN: Shan't. Shan't, shan't, shan't! So there! He's 'orrible.

[*He pokes out his tongue and makes rude faces.*]

H.C.: You nasty little creature.

URCHIN: Crabbyface! Fishy breath! Stinky, stinky!

[*More rude faces and a rude noise.*]

H.C.: Just let me get my claws on him.

[MUSSEL *gets between them.*]

URCHIN: Can't catch me! Silly H.C., can't catch me!

[H.C. *roars and threatens.*]

MUSSEL: It's all right, H.C. I'll deal with him.

H.C.: You'd better. And *quietly*.

[*He retires into his shell, and slams the door.*]

MUSSEL: Just you watch it, Urchin. He's my boss.

URCHIN: Sorry, Mussel.

MUSSEL: He's a very difficult crab.

URCHIN: Sorry, Mussel.

MUSSEL: I'm trying to help you.

URCHIN: Sorry, Mussel.

MUSSEL: And stop saying, 'Sorry, Mussel.'

URCHIN:: Sorry, Mussel. Whoops.

[MUSSEL *can't help smiling.*]

MUSSEL: Come on.

[*Music as they continue the search.*]

BOTH: [*calling*] Auntie Starfish! Auntie Starfish!

[MUSSEL *breaks away to look behind some seaweed.* URCHIN *continues.*]

URCHIN: Auntie Starfish!

[*He approaches the* GIANT ANEMONE, *looks at
it, scratches his head and goes to investigate.
Tension music increases. Hopefully the audience
warns him not to go too close. He stops and backs
away. But he is still curious. He approaches
again. Hopefully the audience stops him.*]

[*This performance could be repeated. Finally*
URCHIN *gets too close; there is a roar from the*
GIANT ANEMONE *and its tentacles start waving.
In the nick of time* MUSSEL *emerges to pull*
URCHIN *clear.*]

MUSSEL: What are you doing now? Never, ever go near that.
That's the Giant Anemone — he can sting you with
his tentacles — paralyse you!

[URCHIN *starts crying.*]

[*Suddenly, from a crevice,* STARFISH *emerges
from the seaweed. She is dazed. She carries a
shell-bag.*]

STARFISH. [*quietly calling*] Urchin! Urchin!

[*During the following speech she sees* URCHIN
and MUSSEL *and assumes* MUSSEL *is hurting*
URCHIN.]

MUSSEL: Now stop crying.

[URCHIN *cries more.*]

You're all right. But I warn you, you're going to get
hurt if you don't watch it. Do you understand?

[*He shakes* URCHIN, *who cries more.* STARFISH
comes to her senses and rushes in to the attack.]

STARFISH: Hey you. Lay off my little nephew. You great bully.

[*She hits* MUSSEL *with her shell-bag.*]

URCHIN: Auntie!

[*He rushes forward.*]

STARFISH: Get out of the way, dear. I'm going to teach this Mussel a lesson.

MUSSEL: Hey!

URCHIN: But Auntie . . .

STARFISH: [*hitting* MUSSEL, *who retreats into his shell.*] You pick on someone your own size. See how *you* like it.

[*Music as* STARFISH *tussles with* MUSSEL, *who is still locked in his shell.*]
Come out and fight. Come on, you coward.

[*She tries to prise him open, but fails, then knocks him over and jumps on him.*]

URCHIN: But Auntie . . .

STARFISH: Shut up, Urchin.

URCHIN: But Auntie . . .

STARFISH: Shut up.

URCHIN:. Mussel was helping me.

STARFISH: I know, dear. He's a big bully, he . . . [*She stops short.*] What?

URCHIN: Mussel was helping me.

STARFISH: Helping you?

URCHIN: Helping me look for you.

STARFISH: Then why was he shouting at you? And why were you crying?

URCHIN: 'Cos I nearly got stung by the Giant Enemy. Mussel saved me.

STARFISH: What Giant Enemy?

URCHIN: [*pointing*] This one.

[*He approaches the* GIANT ANEMONE *just near enough to make it roar and wave its tentacles.*]

STARFISH: Oo er. Come away, dear. It looks dangerous. It might bite.

URCHIN: It can sting you, paralyse you, Mussel says.

STARFISH: [*looking at* MUSSEL] Oh dear.

[MUSSEL *is in his shell, staying still.*]

[*calling*] Mr Mussel.

[*She knocks on his shell.*]

Mr Mussel. I'm so sorry. I had no idea. Mr Mussel.

[*No reaction.*]

[*angrily, to* URCHIN] Why didn't you tell me?

URCHIN: I tried to, Auntie . . .

STARFISH: [*trying again*] Please come out, Mr Mussel. Open up. It was a mistake . . .

[MUSSEL *opens his shell gingerly.*]

Hallo. Please forgive me. I was so worried about little Urchin here, my temper temporarily got the better of me.

[MUSSEL *opens up more.*]

Thank you for helping him.

MUSSEL: That's all right.

STARFISH: Forgive me?

MUSSEL: S'pose so. You nearly split my shell.

STARFISH: Urchin, come and give your Auntie a hug.

[*She envelopes him.*]

I was so worried. Have you been a good boy, dear?

URCHIN: [*muffled*] Yes, Auntie.

[*She squeezes him tighter.*]

STARFISH: [*to* MUSSEL] We were calmly having breakfast in our rockpool, Mr Mussel. Lovely rockpool. Friendly neighbours. Comfortable crevices. Then suddenly, whoosh, this enormous wave crashes in and carries us off. And by the time I'd pulled myself together, Urchin was nowhere to be seen. Disappeared. Hadn't you, dear?

URCHIN: [*muffled*] Yes, Auntie.

STARFISH: Nightmare it was, a real nightmare.

[*She is still clinging to* URCHIN.]

URCHIN: [*muffled*] Auntie, I can't breathe.

[STARFISH *releases him.*]

STARFISH: Sorry, dear. I don't know my own strength.

MUSSEL: You're telling me.

STARFISH: [*opening her shell-bag*] Come and have your medicine, dear.

URCHIN: Oh no, Auntie.

STARFISH: You know it's good for you. [*to* MUSSEL, *showing him a bottle or corked-up shell*] Best seaweed linctus.

URCHIN: But, Auntie, it's got an 'orrible pong.

STARFISH: The nastier it smells, the more good it does you. Drink it.

URCHIN: Shan't.

STARFISH: Listen. Do you want to grow up big and strong like your Auntie Starfish?

URCHIN: Yes.

STARFISH: Then take your medicine.

[*She forces it down him.*]

URCHIN: Ugh!

STARFISH: Fancy some, Mr Mussel?

MUSSEL: Er, no thanks. I've got work to do. So I'll er . . . say goodbye.

[*He starts to move away.*]

STARFISH: Right. Come on, Urchin, let's look for a nice comfy crevice. Over there, maybe. Looks quite sheltered.

[*She leads* URCHIN *off and starts looking behind seaweed.*]

MUSSEL: Hey, what's going on?

STARFISH: We're just getting settled.

MUSSEL: I don't think that's a very good idea.

STARFISH: Eh?

MUSSEL: Well . . . you can't stay here.

STARFISH: Why not? We've nowhere else to stay.

MUSSEL: I know, but . . .

Mussel looks on while Starfish prepares to give Urchin his seaweed linctus.

STARFISH: What?
MUSSEL: Well, *I* wouldn't mind . . . but . . . H.C.
STARFISH: H.C.?
MUSSEL: My boss. He's a hermit crab.
URCHIN: He's 'orrible. He pongs.
STARFISH: Quiet, Urchin.
MUSSEL: He doesn't like strangers.
STARFISH: Strangers? We're not strangers. We're rockpool refugees, we are. Homeless.
MUSSEL: I know, but . . .
STARFISH: Listen, where is this H.C.? I'll soon sort him out.

MUSSEL: No, please.

URCHIN: He lives over there, Auntie, in that shell.

STARFISH: Right. Follow me, Urchin.

> [*She strides over to the shell.* URCHIN *follows. So does* MUSSEL.]

MUSSEL: Please . . .

> [STARFISH *knocks on* H.C.*'s door. No reply. She knocks again. No reply. As she goes to knock again, the door opens and* H.C. *pokes his head out, just in time to be hit on the nose.*]

H.C.: Ow! How dare you!

> [URCHIN *laughs.*]

STARFISH: Shut up, Urchin.

H.C.: Mussel, what's going on?

MUSSEL: Sorry, H.C. This is Starfish.

STARFISH: Good afternoon.

H.C.: What's good about it? What are you doing here?

STARFISH: Well, me and my little nephew Urchin here got washed up by the tide. There was this enormous wave . . .

H.C.: Well?

STARFISH: Well, we wondered, seeing as how we've lost our home, . . . what would you say if we asked, would you mind if we stayed here?

H.C.: I'd say certainly.

STARFISH: Oh thank you.

H.C.: I'd say certainly I *would* mind. I'd mind very much. I don't like strangers.

STARFISH: We wouldn't be strangers once you got to know us.

H.C.: I don't wish to get to know you.

STARFISH: We could work. We could help Mussel.

H.C.: Mussel needs no help. Now please go away. I've got lots of thinking to do.

STARFISH: What sort of thinking?

H.C.: [*after a pause*] I er . . . think about the problems of the world.

STARFISH: Being homeless is a problem.

H.C.: I think about important things. Life.

STARFISH: What about *our* life? Me and little Urchin. Isn't that important?

[*She starts to cry.*]

URCHIN: I told you he was 'orrible.

STARFISH: Shut up, Urchin.

MUSSEL: Couldn't we help them, H.C.? Just this once?

[*Pause.*]

H.C.: Very well. They can stay.

[STARFISH *and* URCHIN *look pleased — but not for long . . .*]

But only till the next tide. Mussel, make sure they catch it.

MUSSEL: Yes, H.C.

[H.C. *goes in and slams the door. Music.* STARFISH *leads* URCHIN *sadly away.* MUSSEL *watches as they go.*]

[*kindly*] Do you want something to eat?

STARFISH: Thank you, Mr Mussel. But I don't feel like eating.

URCHIN: What are we going to do, Auntie?

STARFISH: We'll take our chance with the tide, dear. See where it carries us. Maybe we'll find a friendly rockpool next time.

MUSSEL: I'm sorry.

STARFISH: Not your fault, Mr Mussel.

[*The distant sound of a fog horn. Suddenly* SEAGULL *enters over the back of the rocks.*]

SEAGULL: What ho! Hallo, Mussel.

MUSSEL: You're back are you?

SEAGULL: Yes.

MUSSEL: No tricks this time.

SEAGULL: No, no. Listen, I've got some news. I must tell you. [*seeing* STARFISH *and* URCHIN] Hallo! You weren't here before. Just arrived?

STARFISH: Just going. Thanks to H.C.

URCHIN: He's 'orrible.

SEAGULL: [*impersonating* H.C.] 'I don't stand for strangers in this rockpool.' Right?

STARFISH: Right. We're catching the next tide.

SEAGULL: Ah. Well, I'd tread a bit carefully, if I were you.

STARFISH: How do you mean?

SEAGULL: That's what I came to tell you.
[*Music under speech.*]
[*to* MUSSEL] You see, after I left you, I flew south to the deep sea. To do a spot of fishing, you know. I was high, high in the sky when it suddenly became misty. Foggy, in fact. A real pea-souper. So I lost a bit of height and wheeled and circled and . . . and then I spotted something down below.

MUSSEL: What?

SEAGULL: Terrible kerfuffle. Dreadful mess. These two vast vessels. Two of the biggest ships I'd ever seen. Locked together. Gaping holes in the side. Collided with each other in the fog. Big Ones everywhere. Shouting. Panic. Pandemonium. Frightful mess. I wheeled round and flew back to shore. Nasty business.
[*Short silence.*]

MUSSEL: What's that got to do with us? Sounds like Big Ones' business to me.

URCHIN: I don't like the Big Ones. They're 'orrible.

STARFISH: Shut up, Urchin.

URCHIN: They *are*. They come stomping through our rockpools trying to catch us. Turning over rocks. Messing everything up. That's how I lost my mum and dad, isn't it, Auntie?

STARFISH: [*quietly*] Yes, dear.

MUSSEL: I still don't see what your story's got to do with us, Seagull.

SEAGULL: I'm coming to that, old chap. You see, gushing out of the damaged side of one of the ships was a mighty stream of black stuff . . .

[*Tension chord.*]

MUSSEL: Black stuff?

SEAGULL: Spreading itself over the water like a giant black cloak. Growing and growing. Bigger and bigger. Engulfing the sea. And it seemed to be heading this way . . .

[*The others look anxiously at each other.*]

[*With a roar the* GIANT ANEMONE '*wakes up*' *and waves its tentacles. All jump.*]

Heavens. What's that?

MUSSEL: The Giant Anemone. Wants feeding.

[*He crosses towards it, but stops to collect food.*]

URCHIN: Can I help, Mussel?

MUSSEL: O.K.

STARFISH: Be careful, dear.

[URCHIN *crosses to the* GIANT ANEMONE *to wait. Suddenly* H.C.'*s door opens. He pops out.*]

H.C.: Mussel. Where's my supper?

MUSSEL: [*shouts*] Coming, H.C.

STARFISH: He's just feeding the Giant Anemenemony . . .

H.C.: Hmmm.

[*He suddenly sees* SEAGULL.]

SEAGULL: What ho, H.C.!

H.C.: I thought you'd flown away.

SEAGULL: I flew back.

H.C.: Then fly away again. I . . .

SEAGULL: }
STARFISH: } [*together*] '. . . don't like strangers in this rockpool.'

H.C.: [*retaining his dignity*] Please leave. Now.

SEAGULL: I came to warn you, old chap . . .

H.C.: And I'm warning *you*, [*advancing on* SEAGULL] old chap, to make yourself scarce. Now.
> [*He backs* SEAGULL *towards the* GIANT ANEMONE. MUSSEL *is still collecting food.*]

SEAGULL: All right. All right . . .
> [*He bumps into* URCHIN, *who nearly gets propelled into the* GIANT ANEMONE.]

URCHIN: Aaaaah!
> [MUSSEL *just catches him. The* GIANT ANEMONE *roars.* MUSSEL *throws in some food. Chomping noises. Burp.*]

> [URCHIN *rushes to* STARFISH.]

H.C.: [*to* SEAGULL] Go! Stop causing chaos. Go!

SEAGULL: [*climbing rocks*] I'm off. But don't say I didn't try to warn you.
> [SEAGULL *goes. With a growl,* H.C. *returns to his shell.*]

H.C.: Supper, Mussel.

MUSSEL: Here, H.C.
> [*He dashes over with a shell full of food.* H.C. *receives it, retires, and slams his door.*]

> [*The scene is perceptibly darker now. Night is falling. We can hear the approaching tide.* MUSSEL *raises his eyebrows at* STARFISH.]

It's been one of them days.

STARFISH: I don't know how you stand it.
> [*She looks at* H.C.'s *shell.*]

MUSSEL: H.C.? He's all right usually. No trouble at all. But . . . well . . . the way I see it, there's thinkers and doers.

STARFISH: How do you mean?

MUSSEL: Those as think and those as do. I'm a doer. H.C.'s a thinker. We get on. We're a team.

STARFISH: But you do all the work.

MUSSEL: Exactly. He does all the thinking.

STARFISH: [*after a pause*] Come away with us, Mr Mussel. Start a new life.

MUSSEL: No. No thanks. I belong here. Besides, if I left there'd be no one to feed the Giant Anemone.

STARFISH: H.C.'d have to do it.

MUSSEL: [*with a smile*] No. I'm happy where I am. Really. It's only days like today that . . . well, you know.

[*Pause.*]

STARFISH: I suppose we'd better get ready to go, Urchin.

URCHIN: I don't want to go, Auntie.

MUSSEL: There's a bit of time yet. You have a quick kip. You'll need all your strength later.

[*He yawns.*]

STARFISH: Thank you. Come on, Urchin. Settle down. Oh, you'd better have your medicine first.

URCHIN: Oh, Auntie.

STARFISH: We've got a long journey to face.

[*She gives him his medicine.*]

URCHIN: Ugh.

[*They start to lie down.*]

What about the black stuff, Auntie?

STARFISH: What about it?

MUSSEL: Don't you worry about that. Seagull enjoys telling a story. You could see that. He exaggerated, I expect.

[URCHIN *is not convinced.*]

URCHIN: He said it was heading this way.

MUSSEL: Yes, but it's a long, long way out to sea. Go to sleep.

URCHIN: I'm frightened, Auntie.

MUSSEL: Listen, I'll stay awake and keep watch. O.K.?
STARFISH: Thank you, Mr Mussel.
          [*Music.*]
          Night.
MUSSEL: Night. Night, Urchin.
URCHIN: Night. Night, Auntie.
STARFISH: Night, dear. Sweet dreams.

[*They settle.* MUSSEL *yawns. The noise of the sea increases.* MUSSEL *starts to nod off. He wakes with a start. He yawns again. He falls fast asleep. The lighting fades even more. Silence, but for the noise of the sea.*]

[*A mysterious sound (possibly electronic) accompanied by a tom-tom-sounding heartbeat. From over the rocks wisps of mist appear.*]

[*After a short while,* URCHIN *wakes up. He stands, careful not to wake the others. He suddenly sniffs, an unpleasant smell. He sniffs again, then coughs. He stifles the cough. Then tension music as, through the mist,* SLUDGE *enters, over the rocks. He is dressed in black, with a short ragged cloak. He carries a small tom-tom, shaped like an oil drum, which he bangs in a menacing rhythm.*]

[*The audience may shout a warning. In any event,* URCHIN *turns and sees the visitor. He scuttles away and hides, possibly behind the tin can, but in view of the audience.* URCHIN, *in spite of trying to hold it back, coughs. He stifles it.* SLUDGE *hears it, tenses, stops drumming, and looks about. No sign of anything.*]

[SLUDGE *starts investigating the rockpool. First he sees* H.C.*'s shell and goes to examine it. He gives an oily cackle. Then he crosses stealthily to the sleeping shellfish and examines them. He cackles again.*]

[SLUDGE *approaches the tin can. As he creeps round the back of it,* URCHIN *tiptoes round the front, to avoid him. When he reaches the other end, he involuntarily coughs again.* SLUDGE, *who has emerged round the other end, hears it and freezes. Then he creeps round the front, towards* URCHIN, *who echoes the move by tiptoeing round the back. They swap positions.*]

[*At opposite ends again,* URCHIN *coughs once more.* SLUDGE *freezes, then starts again, creeping round the back.* URCHIN *echoes the move once more, creeping round the front. Halfway he stops and looks back. As he does so,* SLUDGE *re-emerges at the other end, having doubled back.* URCHIN *creeps backwards, unsuspectingly, towards* SLUDGE, *who stealthily advances . . .*]

[*The audience may shout a warning, but it is too late.* SLUDGE *pounces on* URCHIN, *who jumps back, terrified.*]

SLUDGE: Who are you?

URCHIN: [*coughing*] Urchin. Who are you?

SLUDGE: Never you mind. Just stay there and you won't get hurt. Yet.

[*He cackles, and pushes* URCHIN *roughly to the ground. Then he returns to the rocks, and starts beating his tom-tom, as though tapping a message in code.*]

Sludge calling Great Slick. Sludge calling Great Slick. Rockpool ready to receive you. Safe to advance. Safe to advance.

[*With a cackle he disappears over the rocks.*]

[*The noise of the sea increases.* URCHIN *picks himself up and rushes to* STARFISH.]

URCHIN: Auntie! Auntie, wake up!

STARFISH: [*stirring*] Eh? What is it, Urchin?

URCHIN: Quick!

[*He coughs.*]

MUSSEL: [*waking up*] Sorry, I must have nodded off.

STARFISH: [*to* URCHIN] Why are you coughing, Urchin? Are you all right, dear?

URCHIN: No. This stranger came.

MUSSEL: What stranger?

URCHIN: Sludge.

STARFISH: Sludge?

URCHIN: He was 'orrible. All pongy. He made me cough.

STARFISH: Nonsense, dear. You must have been dreaming.

URCHIN: He said the Great Slick's coming.

STARFISH: The Great Slick? What are you talking about?

URCHIN: I don't know, Auntie. Maybe it's the black stuff.

STARFISH: [*worried*] The black stuff? Well, if it *is*, we're not stopping long enough to see it. Come on.

[MUSSEL *goes up the rocks. He has to shout over the noise of the sea.*]

MUSSEL: The tide's coming in fast, Starfish. Time you were off.

[STARFISH *bustles* URCHIN *up the rocks.*]

STARFISH: Right. Over we go. Thank you for everything, Mr Mussel.

MUSSEL: Good luck, Starfish. Mind how you go. Bye, Urchin.

[STARFISH *and* URCHIN *go to jump. A sudden loud noise stops them, a frightening electronic sound. They look down.* STARFISH *screams. All three back away down the rocks in fear.*]

[*Suddenly, over the top of the rocks,* SLUDGE *enters. He beckons. The* GREAT SLICK, *menacing, dressed in black, follows over the rocks.*]

Song: **The Great Slick**

[*During the song, the* GREAT SLICK *advances into the rockpool. He wears an ever-growing black cloak, which covers the area behind him, to represent the oil. If necessary, a couple of 'acolytes' could 'page' the cloak, making it billow.*]

GREAT SLICK: See the great slick
Sticky and thick
Swallowing you whole
If you're not quick.
With my cloak unfurled
I can cover your world.
What a great trick!
What a great slick!

[*By now the* GREAT SLICK *has covered half the rockpool. The shellfish have backed away in terror. They all cough and splutter.*]
There's no escape. I am omnipotent. All in my path must be buried. Alive. Miserable shellfish. Prepare to meet your maker!
[*He starts to move again. Noise. Sea. Electronic. Screams of shellfish.*]

[*Suddenly a flash of lightning hits the rockpool. A blast of thunder. A strong wind. The* GREAT SLICK *reacts. He yells.*]

No! No!

[*More lightning and thunder. The* GREAT SLICK *cowers and starts to retreat. The wind buffets him. He backs away. His cloak retreats.*]

Aaaaaah!

[*He backs up the rocks.*]

I'll be back! I'll be back! I am omnipotent! I will return!

[*Another flash of lightning, more thunder. The* GREAT SLICK *disappears, but the storm continues. The three shellfish run for shelter, fighting against the elements. They are tossed this way and that.*]

[*The tide comes in. Actors make the sheet churn and swell. It engulfs* STARFISH *and* URCHIN, *who flail helplessly, tossed about in the waves.* MUSSEL *tries to reach them, but is suddenly flung towards the* GIANT ANEMONE, *whose tentacles immediately spring to life and try to grab* MUSSEL. *He is caught.* MUSSEL *screams. He tears himself away and collapses, helpless, unable to move. The sea reaches him and covers him. The noise of the storm continues and reaches a climax as the sea tosses wildly.*]

END OF ACT ONE

ACT TWO

Music. Sound effects of the sea. The tide goes out. The
sheet could be manipulated by anonymous stage manage-
ment, or by two or three actors in rehearsal clothes. The
rockpool is revealed again. The tide has caused the tin can
and the flip-flop sole to reposition themselves. Lighting
suggests day — the next morning.
    MUSSEL *lies silent, in view, near the* GIANT
ANEMONE. *Enter* SEAGULL, *rather as he did at the begin-*
ning of the play.

SEAGULL: What ho? Anybody about?
    [*No reply.* SEAGULL *comes down the rocks. He*
    checks that H.C. *isn't waiting for him.*]
    [*calling*] Mussel! Mussel!
    [*No reply. The audience may lead* SEAGULL *to*
    MUSSEL. *In any event, he carries on searching,*
    and finds him.]
    [*approaching*] There you are! Hey, wakey wakey, old
chap. It's morning.
    [MUSSEL *groans and opens his eyes.*]
MUSSEL: [*weak*] Morning, Seagull.
SEAGULL: Rise and shine. Time to get up!
MUSSEL: I don't think I can, Seagull. The storm . . .
SEAGULL: Blew up a bit sharpish, didn't it? I had to take shelter
on land. What happened to you?
MUSSEL: The Giant Anemone. Got tossed onto it. Stung me.
Can't move.
SEAGULL: You poor chap. What can I do?

[*Suddenly we hear the voice of* STARFISH, *as she emerges from the tin can.*]

STARFISH: [*calling*] Mr Mussel! Mr Mussel!

SEAGULL: Over here.

STARFISH: Oh, it's you, Seagull. [*calling inside the tin*] It's all right dear, you can come out. The storm's over.

[URCHIN *emerges. They go over to* SEAGULL *and* MUSSEL.]

SEAGULL: I'm afraid Mussel's in a bad way. The Giant Anemone got him.

URCHIN: Is he dead?

SEAGULL: No, no!

STARFISH: [*examining* MUSSEL] He'll be out of action for a while. Till the sting wears off. It's all right, Mr Mussel. We'll look after you. Have some of Urchin's medicine. It'll help. It's very powerful.

[*She takes some from her shell-bag and gives it to him.*]

MUSSEL: Ugh!

STARFISH: Now try to rest.

MUSSEL: [*whispers*] Thank you, Starfish.

SEAGULL: Lucky you were still here. I thought you were catching the tide.

STARFISH: Didn't you see? The Great Slick came.

SEAGULL: The Great Slick?

URCHIN: The black stuff. Tried to swallow us all up.

STARFISH: The storm frightened him away. The wind forced him back out to sea.

URCHIN: He's got an 'orrible pong. Makes you cough.

STARFISH: What's worse, he said he'd be back.

URCHIN: I want to go.

STARFISH: Don't be silly, Urchin. There's nowhere we *can* go. Till the tide comes.

SEAGULL: And by the sound of it, the Great Slick will come with it. You're in danger.

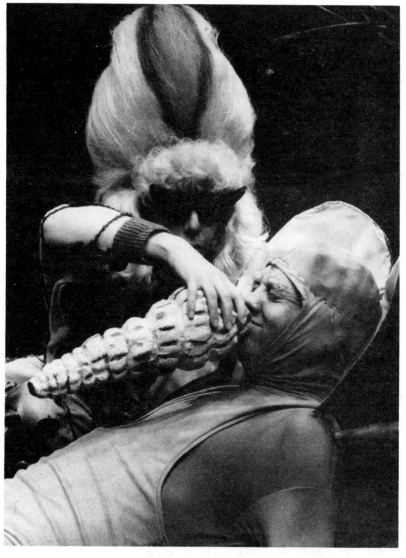

'*It's all right, Mr Mussel,*' *says Starfish,* '*We'll look after you. Have some of Urchin's medicine. It'll help you. It's very powerful.*'

[STARFISH *nods.*]

URCHIN: Oh Auntie.

[*She comforts him. The sudden roar of the* GIANT ANEMONE *diverts their thoughts.*]

STARFISH: That great monster's woken up now.

URCHIN: I'll feed it, Auntie. I know where Mussel keeps the food.

STARFISH: All right, dear. But be careful.

SEAGULL: Listen, I'll nip off and see what the tide's up to. Check the wind direction.

STARFISH: Thanks, Seagull.

SEAGULL: My pleasure.

[*He exits up and over the rocks. The* GIANT ANEMONE *roars again.* URCHIN *finds food for it, and carefully throws it in. Chomping noises. Burp.*]

[*Suddenly* H.C.*'s door opens. He pops out.*]

H.C.: Mussel, where's my breakfast?

MUSSEL: [*involuntarily, weak*] Coming, H.C.

STARFISH: It's all right, Mr. Mussel. I'll look after him. [*calling*] Coming, H.C.

[*She crosses to* H.C.*'s shell.* URCHIN *hovers.*] Morning, H.C.

H.C.: Where's Mussel?

STARFISH: I'm afraid he's out of action for a while, H.C. You'll have to make do with me. [*calling*] Urchin, will you get H.C.'s breakfast, please dear?

URCHIN: Yes, Auntie.

[*He does so.*]

H.C.: What's the matter with Mussel?

STARFISH: The Giant Anemone, that's what. Stung him in the storm.

H.C.: Storm. What storm?

STARFISH: Don't tell me you missed the storm?

H.C.: And why are you still here?

STARFISH: Just as well we *are* still here, isn't it? Otherwise you'd have no breakfast.

[URCHIN *hands it to him.*]

H.C.: [*grudgingly*] Mm. Thank you.

STARFISH: Don't thank me, thank the Great Slick. We'd have gone long ago if it hadn't been for him.

H.C.: The Great Slick?

URCHIN: Nasty black stuff trying to cover the rockpool. He's coming to get you.

STARFISH: He's coming to get all of us.

H.C.: I don't know what you're talking about. Black stuff?

STARFISH: You don't *want* to know, you mean.

H.C.: I haven't got time to listen to this rubbish. If you ask me, this is a trick. You and that wretched Urchin want to stay here, in my rockpool, so you invent silly stories. Storm, Great Slick, black stuff. It wouldn't surprise me to learn that you put Mussel up to this. It's a conspiracy. To annoy me.

URCHIN: It's not. It's true.

H.C.: Go away. I don't want to hear another word. I'm try- ing to *think*.

STARFISH: Oh yes. 'The problems of the world'. 'Life'. Well, why don't you try thinking about the problems of life in your rockpool? Eh? There won't *be* a rockpool if the Great Slick has his way. Just a mass of thick, sticky, black stuff. Is that what you want?

[*Pause.* H.C. *turns huffily to leave.*]

Going back in eh? Going to have a *think* about it? By the time you've had your think, it may be too late.

H.C.: [*tense*] All I want is to be left in peace.

STARFISH: Oh yes. Live in *peace*. And leave the wars to others. Us. Leave us to do the dirty work. You're the most selfish shellfish it's been my misfortune to meet.

'All I want is to be left in peace,' grumbles H.C. Starfish is outraged: 'You're the most selfish shellfish it's been my misfortune to meet.'

H.C.: Nobody asked you to meet me. Nobody asked you to come here. Nobody's asking you to stay. Good morning.
[*He slams the door, taking his breakfast with him.*]

[SEAGULL *returns over the rocks.*]
SEAGULL: What ho? Told H.C.?
STARFISH: Sort of.
URCHIN: He wouldn't believe us.

SEAGULL: Well, that's his look-out. Hey, and talking of look-
outs, I'm sorry to say you were right. The Great
Slick's on his way.

STARFISH: How long have we got?

SEAGULL: Not that long, I'm afraid.

URCHIN: What are we going to do, Auntie?

STARFISH: Not much we can do. Except wait.

SEAGULL: Hang on. You could try evacuation.

URCHIN: What's that?

SEAGULL: You could leave.

STARFISH: Don't be silly, we'd go slap into the Great Slick.

SEAGULL: No. You misunderstand me. You could go the other
way.

[*He points towards the audience.*]

STARFISH: Up the beach? We couldn't survive up there.

SEAGULL: Just a little way up. On the tide line. With luck, the
Great Slick won't come that far. What do you think?

STARFISH: It's worth a try.

URCHIN: What about Mussel?

STARFISH: He can come too.

URCHIN: But he can't move, Auntie.

STARFISH: We'll manage somehow. Thank you, Seagull.

SEAGULL: What about H.C.?

STARFISH: He wouldn't come.

SEAGULL: Leave him to take his chance, eh?

URCHIN: We tried to warn him.

STARFISH: Right. Come on, then.

[*Music. In a 'silent' sequence,* STARFISH *and*
URCHIN, *watched and helped by* SEAGULL,
prepare to leave. They go to MUSSEL; *he is still
motionless. They try to lift him, but he is too
cumbersome.* SEAGULL *has an idea. He indicates
the flip-flop sole.* STARFISH *and* URCHIN *fetch it,*

Mussel lies paralysed having been stung by the Giant Anemone, while Seagull brings the news that the Great Slick is coming.

and carefully roll MUSSEL *on to it. Using it as a stretcher they set off downstage — 'up the beach'. If possible, they should negotiate a few rocks or other obstacles.* SEAGULL *leads the way. Perhaps* URCHIN *stumbles. Eventually they reach the edge of the rockpool, climb over, and arrive, tired, on the 'beach' — on the extreme downstage area. They lay* MUSSEL *down.*]

All right, Mr Mussel?

MUSSEL: Yes, thanks. I can feel a bit of movement coming back.

[*With an effort he manages to roll slightly.*]

STARFISH: Good.

MUSSEL: Where are we?

SEAGULL: Up the beach. Safest place.

MUSSEL: H.C. Where's H.C.?

STARFISH: He didn't believe there was any danger. He'll have to take his chance.

URCHIN: What do we do now, Auntie?

STARFISH: Just wait, I suppose.

SEAGULL: Waiting's always the worst part.

URCHIN: Do you think Sludge will come too?

SEAGULL: Sludge?

URCHIN: I told you. He works for the Great Slick. I saw him. He arrives first, checks the coast's clear, then bangs a message on his drum. Then the Great Slick comes.

STARFISH: Are you sure you weren't dreaming, dear? *We* never saw him.

URCHIN: You were asleep.

SEAGULL: How big is this Sludge?

URCHIN: Bit bigger than me.

SEAGULL: If we could get rid of him somehow, maybe the Great Slick wouldn't come.

URCHIN: You mean, stop Sludge sending his message?

SEAGULL: Exactly.

URCHIN: Yes!

STARFISH: But how could we get rid of him? We'd have to catch him first.

MUSSEL: [*with an effort*] The tin can. The Big Ones' rubbish.

URCHIN: Of course! The tin can! Mussel's right, Auntie. He'd fit in there. Then you and I could roll him over the rocks and away.

SEAGULL: That might work.

STARFISH: But how do we get him in the tin can in the first place?

URCHIN: I'll pretend I'm in there, call out, and he'll come and look. Then I'll rush out and shut him in.

STARFISH: Sounds risky to me. Suppose he thinks it's a trap? He might not believe you.

[URCHIN *has an idea: he turns to the audience.*]

URCHIN: He might not believe me, but he'd believe *them!* Would you help us, please?

AUDIENCE: Yes.

URCHIN: You will?

AUDIENCE: Yes.

URCHIN: If he's suspicious, make him go in the tin can, right?

[*Suddenly the noise of the sea increases. The ominous sound of drumming heralds* SLUDGE'*s arrival.*]

He's coming!

[*He scampers off back into the rockpool.*]

STARFISH: Good luck, dear.

[*The others watch as* URCHIN *hides behind the tin can (the downstage side).* MUSSEL *manages to sit up. The lights fade.*]

[*Enter, stealthily,* SLUDGE, *beating his drum. Tension music increases.* SLUDGE *quickly checks the rockpool to see that the coast is clear. He cackles.*]

SLUDGE: Right, rockpool. Get ready. The Great Slick is all-powerful. You can't escape him twice.

[*He goes to bang his drum.* URCHIN *coughs, cupping his hands in front of his mouth to make the sound 'hollow'.* SLUDGE *stops.* URCHIN *coughs again.*]

What's that noise?

URCHIN: Help! Help!

SLUDGE: Who is it?

[*He encourages the audience to tell him.*]

Anyone know? Who is it?

AUDIENCE: Urchin.

SLUDGE: Who?

AUDIENCE: Urchin.

SLUDGE: Urchin? That nasty little shellfish I met last time!
Now's my chance to finish him off. [*He cackles.*]
Where is he?

        [*If necessary,* STARFISH, MUSSEL *and* SEAGULL
        lead the audience.]

AUDIENCE: In the tin can.

SLUDGE: Where?

AUDIENCE: In the tin can.

        [SLUDGE *looks around and sees it.*]

SLUDGE: In there?

AUDIENCE: Yes.

URCHIN: [*coughing*] Help! Help!

SLUDGE: Right, my little friend. I'll give you help.

        [*He cackles*]

        [*Tension music as he puts down his drum and
        approaches the tin can.* URCHIN *moves round the
        end of the can to avoid being seen. Suddenly*
        SLUDGE *stops.*]
        This isn't a trap, is it?

AUDIENCE: No.

SLUDGE: Are you sure?

AUDIENCE: Yes.

        [SLUDGE *slowly enters the tin can. But just as he
        does so,* H.C. *suddenly pops out of his shell.*]

H.C.: What's happening? What's this appalling row?

STARFISH: Oh no, he'll ruin everything.

URCHIN: [*coming from behind the tin can*] Back, H.C., *please*, go
back.

H.C.: Oh it's you, is it? I might have known.

URCHIN: Shhhh! Please.

[*He struggles to close the tin lid.*]

H.C.: Don't you shush me. Nobody shushes me.

[SLUDGE *pops out of the tin.*]

SLUDGE: Oh no?

URCHIN: Oh no!

[*He runs to hide.*]

H.C.: Who are you?

SLUDGE: Never you mind.

H.C.: I *do* mind. I most certainly *do* mind. I will not have strangers in my rockpool. [*He coughs.*] What's that smell?

SLUDGE: Me.

H.C.: [*coughs*] Go away. I'm about to lose my temper.

SLUDGE: You're about to lose your rockpool.

[*Music, as* SLUDGE *waves his black cloak in* H.C.*'s face.* H.C. *coughs and splutters. Then he springs at* SLUDGE *and misses —* SLUDGE *uses his cloak like a bullfighter.* H.C. *turns and springs again. Again he misses.* H.C. *springs a third time. This time he falls. He coughs.* SLUDGE *taunts him with the cloak, covering him, then whisking it off again. He cackles, enjoying* H.C.*'s discomfort.*]

[*Suddenly* URCHIN *emerges from hiding.* SLUDGE *has his back to him.* URCHIN *bravely kicks* SLUDGE *up the backside.* SLUDGE *reacts and turns. He sees* URCHIN.]

Why, you . . .

[*He advances on* URCHIN.]

STARFISH: Urchin!

[STARFISH *decides she ought to help, and creeps down and round the rockpool.* H.C. *continues to cough and stays on the ground. Meanwhile, exciting music as a chase develops.* SLUDGE *chases* URCHIN *round the rockpool, round the tin can, etc. Then* URCHIN *hides in the tin can.* SLUDGE *can't find him.* SLUDGE *comes forward.*]

SLUDGE: [*to the audience*] Where is he?

[URCHIN *pops out of the can and, unseen by* SLUDGE *downstage of him, indicates to the audience that they should tell* SLUDGE *that* URCHIN *is in the can. Hopefully they do this. In any event,* URCHIN *coughs, then hides behind the can.* SLUDGE *hears the audience and/or the cough, and rushes into the can with a roar. Immediately,* URCHIN *dashes out to close the lid;* STARFISH *runs to join him. They manage to close the lid.* SLUDGE *roars inside.*]

[URCHIN *and* STARFISH *roll the tin can up and over the rocks. It disappears. Musical fanfare. They congratulate each other.* MUSSEL *and* SEAGULL *applaud from the 'beach'. Music continues as* STARFISH *and* URCHIN *help* H.C. *up, and escort him up to the others. As they go,* URCHIN *spots* SLUDGE's *drum, and picks it up.*]

MUSSEL: All in one piece, H.C.?

H.C.: A trifle shaken, I'm afraid, Mussel. Took me by surprise.

SEAGULL: We tried to warn you.

STARFISH: But you wouldn't listen.

H.C.: I know. I know. I . . . apologise.

STARFISH: You had lots of thinking to do . . .

H.C.: Too much thinking. Thinking wouldn't have got me out of trouble just then. [*genuinely*] Thank you. Thank you for saving me.

STARFISH: We couldn't just leave you.

H.C.: I didn't deserve it. I er . . . haven't treated *you* very kindly, I know. I was very selfish. Listen, if you and

Urchin would like it, you'd be very welcome to stay in my rockpool.

STARFISH: Thank you, H.C.

URCHIN: But is it safe, Auntie?

H.C.: No danger now, thanks to you. The Great Slick's gone for good.

URCHIN: Eh?

H.C.: You got rid of him. Over the rocks. Thanks to you, we're safe.

MUSSEL: But H.C., that wasn't the Great Slick.

STARFISH: That was only Sludge.

H.C.: You mean there's more?

MUSSEL: Listen H.C., last night, the Great Slick nearly covered the rockpool.

URCHIN: And us. He's huge. Black stuff. If it hadn't been for the storm . . .

H.C.: But where does this black stuff come from?

SEAGULL: Two big ships out at sea. Collision, H.C. Black stuff spurting from the side.

H.C.: Big Ones' rubbish again. Might have known it. Where is it now?

STARFISH: Heading this way.

SEAGULL: I'll go and check its position.

[*He leaves, crosses the rockpool and looks over the rocks.*]

URCHIN: Sludge didn't send him his message this time. I've got his drum, look.

MUSSEL: No, but we can't be sure he won't attack anyway.

SEAGULL: [*calling*] He's still there. And the tide's still coming in. I'll stay here and keep look-out.

[*He disappears from view behind the rocks.*]

STARFISH: [*calling*] O.K., Seagull.

[*Suddenly the booming voice of the* GREAT SLICK *from a distance makes all jump.*]

GREAT SLICK: [*calling*] Sludge! Sludge! Where are you. Over!

[*Silence.*]
Are you in difficulty? Over!
MUSSEL: What are we going to do, H.C.?
H.C.: [*crossly*] How should I know?
STARFISH: Please, H.C. You're a thinker, aren't you?
[H.C. *nods.*]
Then think of a plan. Quick.
H.C.: Very well, I'll try. Now . . . he's had no message from Sludge, right?
URCHIN: Right.
H.C.: So he might not come.
STARFISH: Right.
H.C.: On the other hand, he might come *looking* for Sludge.
MUSSEL: Right.
H.C.: And even if he doesn't, he still poses a future threat.
MUSSEL: He could destroy the rockpool.
STARFISH: He could destroy *us*.
H.C.: But aren't we safe up here?
MUSSEL: Hopefully yes, but with a strong tide anything's possible.
[*Pause.*]
H.C.: There's only one thing for it.
STARFISH: Yes?
H.C.: We must invite him to come. Send a message on his drum.
URCHIN: I could do that. I heard Sludge do it last night.
H.C.: Excellent.
MUSSEL: But why, H.C.? Why invite him to come?
H.C.: Because we've got to get rid of him once and forever.
STARFISH: Yes, but how?
H.C.: You said he came last night.
STARFISH: Yes.
H.C.: What made him leave? Why didn't he destroy the rockpool there and then?
URCHIN: Of course, the storm!

H.C.: The storm, I see.

MUSSEL: The wind made the tide turn. The Great Slick was carried off with it.

H.C.: There must be another storm. A storm so violent, he'll never dare to return.

STARFISH: But we can't just make a storm happen.

[*Pause.* URCHIN *suddenly turns to the audience.*]

URCHIN: *We* can't. But *they* could!

H.C.: How?

URCHIN: They could make *noises* like a storm. Big, frightening noises. [*to the audience*] Will you help us again?

AUDIENCE: Yes.

URCHIN: You will?

AUDIENCE: Yes!

URCHIN: Thank you.

H.C.: Excellent. Let's get organised. What do we need first?

MUSSEL: Lightning.

H.C.: Lightning. [*referring to the audience*] They can't do the light part — the flash.

STARFISH: No, but they could make the sound. Like this. [*She claps.*] Everybody clap — just once. After three. One, two, three.

[*The audience claps.*]

Very good. Once more. After three. One, two, three.

[*The audience claps.*]

Thank you.

H.C.: Next.

MUSSEL: Thunder.

URCHIN: Ooh, thunder, can I do this one, H.C.?

H.C.: Certainly.

URCHIN: Right. [*to the audience*] Now, when I say 'go', I want everyone to stamp on the floor —

[*He demonstrates.*]

One, two, three, go!

[*The audience stamps.*]

Great! Now, listen, let's try again; let's try to start sort of soft and distant and then build it up and up to being loud. Right. Ready? One, two, three, go.

[*He directs the audience to stamp softly, getting louder.*]

Yes! Thank you.

H.C.: Next?

MUSSEL: The wind, H.C.

H.C.: Ah yes. You lead that one, Mussel.

MUSSEL: Right, H.C. [*He struggles to his feet.*] I think I'm feeling strong enough . . . to stand!

STARFISH: Good for you, Mr Mussel.

MUSSEL: [*to the audience*] Right, let's have a really strong wind. When I say go, blow wind, blow. One, two, three, go!

[*The audience is encouraged to blow.*]

Louder! Howling wind!

[*They blow more.*]

Lovely! Thank you.

H.C.: Excellent. Now, let's put them all together and see what we have —

STARFISH: Lightning.

URCHIN: Thunder.

MUSSEL: Wind.

H.C.: Ready, steady, go!

[STARFISH *steps foward and leads the lightning noise. Then* URCHIN *steps forward and leads the thunder noise. Then* MUSSEL *hobbles forward and leads the wind.*]

Excellent! Well done. We're ready for him. Urchin. Send the message.

[*Music as* URCHIN *positions himself with* SLUDGE's *drum. The others give him encouraging looks. He bangs a rhythm, then imitates* SLUDGE's *voice.*]

URCHIN: Sludge calling Great Slick. Sludge calling Great Slick. Rockpool ready to receive you. Safe to advance. Safe to advance.

[*He returns to the others.*]

STARFISH: Well done, dear.

URCHIN: Thanks, Auntie.

[*Tension music starts.*]

H.C.: Now, let's see if he comes. [*to the audience*] Good luck everybody. Mussel, you give them a signal. [*to the audience*] Wait for the signal and give the Great Slick the fright of his life! Get rid of him!

[SEAGULL *appears on the rocks.*]

SEAGULL: [*loud whisper*] He's coming!

[*He disappears over the rocks. Music and sound effects increase. Lights fade. The* GREAT SLICK *enters, over the rocks.*]

Song: **The Great Slick**

[*During the song he moves slowly but surely downstage. If necessary, his 'acolytes' help spread his cloak over the rockpool.*]

GREAT SLICK: See the great slick
Sticky and thick
Swallowing you whole
If you're not quick.
With my cloak unfurled
I can cover your world.
What a great trick!
What a great slick!

[*By the end of the song his cloak covers three quarters of the rockpool.*]

I am omnipotent. Nothing in this rockpool will be

spared. My oil will seep into every crevice and suffocate every living animal and plant. The Great Slick rules!
[*Music. The* GREAT SLICK *starts his advance again.*]

MUSSEL: [*to the audience*] Now!
[*The audience, led by* STARFISH, URCHIN *and* MUSSEL, *do their noises.*
Lightning noise.
Thunder noise.
Wind noise.
Sound effects echo the GREAT SLICK'*s reactions.*
He quivers and quakes.]

GREAT SLICK: No! No!
[*He reacts. He holds his ears. He reacts as though buffeted by the wind.*]
Help! Help!
[*His cloak retreats with him. Finally he disappears.*]
Aaaaaaaaaah!
[*All turn to the audience and cheer.*]

ALL: Thank you! You did it! Well done!
[*But the tension noise starts again. Unseen by the shellfish, the* GREAT SLICK *returns, and looks suspiciously from the top of the rocks. The audience hopefully points this out to the shellfish, who eventually turn and see him.*]

GREAT SLICK: [*with a roar*] Ha, ha! I might have guessed. There was no storm at all. It was all those snivelling creatures *pretending* to be a storm with their silly noises. You cannot trick the Great Slick! You will all pay. I will advance and swallow you *all*! Ha, ha, ha.
[*Music. The* GREAT SLICK *advances. The shellfish scatter in terror into the audience. The music heightens as the* GREAT SLICK *gets nearer.*]

[*Then, suddenly,* SEAGULL *enters over the rocks. He stumbles with difficulty over the* GREAT SLICK's *cloak, till he reaches him. He attacks him with his beak from behind. In a mimed choreographed sequence, the* GREAT SLICK *reacts and a fight develops. The* GREAT SLICK *tries to engulf* SEAGULL *in his cloak.* SEAGULL *tries to avoid him, yet force him to retreat. The shellfish shout encouragement to* SEAGULL . *But, eventually,* SEAGULL *is engulfed under the cloak. He disappears.*]

GREAT SLICK: [*manic*] I am omnipotent! The Great Slick rules! Ha, ha, ha.

[*With manic cackling, he advances again. He nears the edge of the rockpool. Then suddenly there is a flash of lightning. The* GREAT SLICK *stops, unsure. A* real *storm comes. Loud claps of thunder. Howling wind. The* GREAT SLICK *reacts, furious but powerless. He backs away. Then, affected by the wind, he suddenly starts turning and twisting uncontrollably, like a whirlpool. This has the effect of gathering in his cloak tighter and tighter round his body. He nearly loses his balance, tries to retreat, but is driven towards the* GIANT ANEMONE. *He hits it. The* GIANT ANEMONE *roars. Its tentacles wave and strike the* GREAT SLICK, *who reacts to the stinging. He screams. The* GIANT ANEMONE's *mouth opens and shuts menacingly. Finally, the* GREAT SLICK *is dragged unceremoniously through the* GIANT ANEMONE's *mouth. He is devoured. Chomping noises. Big burp. Silence.*]

[*In the audience the shellfish cheer.*]

H.C.: He's gone!

ALL: Hooray!
STARFISH: Thank you, storm!
ALL: Hooray!
MUSSEL: Thank you, Giant Anemone!
ALL: Hooray!
URCHIN: [*to the audience*] Thank *you*!
ALL: Hooray!
H.C.: We can go home!
ALL: Hooray!

[*They all reach the edge of the rockpool and start to go back in. As they face upstage, they suddenly stop.*]

[*Music as* SEAGULL *enters at the top of the rocks. He wears a black cloak of 'oil'. He stumbles painfully to the centre of the pool. The others watch in stunned silence.* SEAGULL *collapses. He has a couple of convulsions, and is then still.* STARFISH *rushes to him. She listens to his chest, then looks at the others and shakes her head. He is dead. The shellfish move sadly to each other, humming the 'When will we learn' tune. They all hold hands, in grief. Then they continue humming, while removing part of their costume. Actors' heads are revealed. It is now clear that the actors have come out of character. Only* SEAGULL *remains centre stage.*]

Song: **When will we learn?**

ALL: [*softly*] When will we learn?
When will we learn?
That the world
Wasn't made
For only you and me?
When will we learn?

When will it be?
When will we learn?
When will we see?

> [*Two actors go to* SEAGULL *and hold out their
> arms.* SEAGULL *gets up, and removes part of his
> costume. He is an actor again. All join and
> sing.*]

[*louder*] When will we learn?
When will we learn?
That the world
Wasn't made
For only you and me?
When will we learn?
When will it be?
When will we learn?
When will we see?

Will we ever stop polluting
The rivers and the seas?
Will we ever stop destroying
The forests and the trees?

When will we learn?
When will we learn?
That the world
Wasn't made
For only you and me?
When will we learn?
When will it be?
When will we learn?
When will we see?

Do we care about the tiger?
And will we save the whale?
Can we really say we're trying?
Or are we bound to fail?

With our poison or detergent
Insecticide or spray
Are we killing our tomorrow
By living for today?

When will we learn?
When will we learn?
That the world
Wasn't made
For only you and me?
When will we learn?
When will it be?
When will we learn?
When will we see?

When will we learn?
How long must we wait?
And if we do learn
Will it be too late?

When will we learn?

THE END